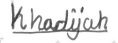

Khadijah

Imam Hussein

may Allah be pleased with him

Attiyah Rashid

Ta-Ha Publishers Ltd.
www.taha.co.uk

Copyright © Ta-Ha Publishers Ltd 1413AH/1993CE

Reprinted 1997, 2006

Published by:
Ta-Ha Publishers Ltd.
1 Wynne Road
London SW9 0BB

Website: http://www.taha.co.uk/
Email: sales@taha.co.uk

British Library Cataloguing in Publication Data
Rashid, Attiyah
Story of Imam Hussein
I Title
297.092

ISBN 0 907461 96 4

Printed and Bound in England by: De-Luxe Printers Ltd.

It was a hot evening in Madinah as the sounds of a young girl's crying floated over the market place.

"That poor girl," commented an old man, "these are dark days for her now that her father is dead." As an afterthought he added, "In fact these are dark days for all of us."

"Was her father someone important then?" enquired a nearby stranger.

"You mean to say you don't know?" exclaimed the old man.

"I am a traveller, I have no knowledge of current events," he explained.

"Oh I see," conceded the elder. "It's just that the young girl whom we can hear sobbing is the daughter of our beloved Prophet's grandson, may the blessings and peace of Allah be on him and his family - Imam Hussein, who has only recently been killed in battle."

This was indeed news to the traveller who could hardly believe his ears.

"How did it happen?" he asked.

"In the most tragic of ways," replied the old man shaking his head sorrowfully. Looking up at the young man, he said, "Why don't you come to my house for dinner and I can explain the whole thing to you."

The traveller agreed and after a hearty meal and prayers the two men sat in the cool evening air - the old Arab re-telling the events that had recently taken place, while the young foreigner listened attentively.

"You are a very young man and perhaps do not know the history of how these things came about, so I will begin at the beginning," commenced the old man. "It all really started with the Prophet Muhammad's death, may Allah bless him and grant him peace. It was hard for everyone to accept that he was really going to leave us - those were the most testing times. I can still remember the time when our dear 'Umar stood up in the mosque and proclaimed that if anyone were even to mention that the Prophet was going to die, then he would personally chop their heads off for entertaining such implausible thoughts!

"Abu Bakr soon set him straight though. He spoke

logically, explaining that eventually everyone has to rejoin Allah - even the Prophet, and that no matter how hard it seemed, we had to accept it and see it as a joyful time for the Prophet who was with Allah.

"I think it was then really that we knew it would be Abu Bakr, may Allah be pleased with him, who was to be the first Khalif. He always led the prayers when the Prophet, may Allah bless him and grant him peace, was ill, and was obviously considered the best choice.

"During Abu Bakr's time the days were truly golden; he led the Muslims well and Islam spread swiftly with new additions being made far and wide. Those days were both profitable and peaceful but alas Abu Bakr too had to leave this earth. Before he died he appointed 'Umar, may Allah be pleased with him, as the next Khalif. 'Umar at first declined the role saying his temper was too short and that he had certain qualms about being a good leader. Abu Bakr, however, convinced 'Umar that he would learn to control his temper and that he would be able to lead the Muslims well.

"He was not wrong. 'Umar's rule was a remarkably successful one. Any worries he might have had about his abilities as a Khalif were totally unfounded; he led us well, introducing various systems so that the poor wouldn't go hungry, so that widows were looked after and so that basically justice was upheld. He was a very fair man and for this reason he was known as 'Umar

Farooq, may Allah be pleased with him."

The traveller raised an enquiring eye at this.

"It means 'Umar, the one who is just," explained the elder. "There are countless tales of his kind doings, although I will not go into them just now. Suffice it to say he was a true Khalif, living honestly and simply; but sadly it was his justice itself which ended his life.

"The story goes that there was some sort of dispute between a Muslim and a Jew - I'm not quite clear what it was about - but anyway, it was all becoming rather heated, so 'Umar, may Allah be pleased with him, stepped in to settle the argument. I suppose you might imagine that he would automatically defend the Muslim without thinking? But oh no! He was much too fair for that. He sorted it out properly by listening to both sides of the argument, and found that it was in fact the Muslim and not the Jew who was at fault. 'Umar met his fate at the hand of Abu Lu'lu'a Fairuz, a Persian slave, but the slave was part of a conspiracy with Hurmuzan to kill him."

The old man paused for a moment, an expression of pain on his face at the thought of what he had just retold. Then, because it hurt him too much to dwell upon it, he continued quickly saying, "As you can see, it was an awful time - we just could not believe that someone could do such a thing to a Khalif, to a successor of our beloved Prophet, may Allah bless him and grant him peace. But still, I'm ashamed to say, it happened and now a new Khalif had to be chosen."

"Who was it this time - Ali?" asked the traveller.

The old man shook his head, "No, next came 'Uthman, the Generous, may Allah be pleased with him.

"'Uthman was a good man also, as were all the early Khalifs. He was a very generous and forgiving man – some say rather too forgiving.

"When he became the Khalif, Islam, as I have told you, had been spread far and wide. 'Uthman therefore had to appoint several able men to help govern the various countries which were now part of the Islamic community. One of these men was Mu'awiya who became the governor of Syria. He was the son of Abu Sufyan - an uncle of the Prophet, may Allah bless him and grant him peace - who opposed the Prophet for many years and did not accept Islam until the conquest of Makkah.

"His son Mu'awiya was different though - he had accepted Islam as the true religion well before his father and was a good Muslim. Mu'awiya's son, Yazeed, however, seemed to possess some of the habits that people had in the time of ignorance before Islam. He drank wine and kept women. Such rumours we would hear of him! No, no one in their right mind could have called Yazeed a good man…"

"Yazeed did you say?" interjected the younger man, "But he's the present…"

"Yes yes," snapped the old man, annoyed, "but don't interrupt; all will become clear soon enough. Now where was I? Oh yes, Yazeed. Unfortunately he was not the only one not to follow the path of Islam correctly. There was and still is, an increasing number of unbelievers within the Muslim countries who wanted to overthrow Islamic rule, usually attempting to do so by murder and violence. They plotted against 'Uthman, may Allah be pleased with him, spreading rumours and lies about him and just generally undermining his authority by questioning his ability as a Khalif.

"Now I've already told you that 'Uthman had the tendency to forgive and forget rather easily. Well there came a time when an Amir chose unfortunately to indulge in some rather crooked business, and in order to do it he used the official Seal of the Khalif without permission.

"Obviously when this was discovered, things came to a head. Everyone thought that 'Uthman would throw the man out, but instead, after listening to the man's pleas and promises that such an occurrence would never happen again, 'Uthman, may Allah be pleased with him, chose to keep him on.

"Of course this was a golden opportunity for the unbelievers to make a fuss and they did not waste it. 'Uthman, however, stuck to his decision and said that he was entitled to give the man a second chance. Shortly after this, a group of four unbelievers set upon the beloved Khalif and whilst he was reading the Holy Qur'an, they assassinated him."

"Another Khalif murdered?" asked the young listener incredulously.

"I'm afraid so, hard though it is to accept that such brutality is possible. But I shall move on now to 'Ali's rule, for he was made Khalif next, may Allah be pleased with him.

"When 'Ali was chosen as the Khalif, there were a lot of civil wars and battles going on between the real Muslims and those who were not really Muslims, making it all in all a very difficult time. The unbelievers, particularly from Syria, were becoming worse and worse and were doing everything they could to try and undermine Islamic power.

"Those were awful days, with fighting going on all the time. There was even a battle between 'Aishah and 'Ali, may Allah be pleased with them both!"

"What, 'Aishah the Prophet's wife?" asked the young man.

"Yes, almost unbelievably so. It seems she felt 'Ali was not doing his job well enough, or some such dispute. The argument was resolved though, after 'Ali, may Allah be pleased with him, reminded 'Aishah's followers of some sacred words of the Prophet, may Allah bless him and grant him peace, and 'Aishah admitted she was wrong, may Allah be pleased with her.

"After a few years of rule, though, even 'Ali, may Allah be pleased with him, was killed. This time it happened in a crowded mosque; he was stabbed to death with poisoned daggers at the hands of the unbelievers.

"Poisoned daggers - can you believe it? Do these people have no conscience? Still those evil sinners will pay dearly in the fires of Hell in the next life!

"The only consolation, after having three rightly-guided Khalifs murdered, is that they died as martyrs in the way of Allah, which is the best way to die, and went straight to Paradise!

"Once more a Khalif had to be chosen and this time Yazeed made it clear that he desired the title. Unfortunately for him, but luckily for the rest of us, Imam Hassan - 'Ali's son and the Prophet's grandson, may the blessings and peace of Allah be on him and all his family, was chosen."

"Hassan not Hussein?" queried the traveller.

"That's right. Hassan and Hussein were brothers, may Allah be pleased with them, but Hassan was the older so he was chosen as the next Khalif. But, unfortunately, I have to tell you that his rule also was cut short. It all came about in the most treacherous of ways - he was poisoned, some say by his own wife!"

"Apparently the woman's mind was corrupted - by whom I'm not sure exactly; some say it was the work of the unbelievers, while others think that Yazeed's men were responsible. I myself go with the latter explanation because soon after the murder of Hassan, may Allah be pleased with him, Yazeed invaded the Muslim lands with his armed forces and appointed himself as the new Khalif. Some Khalif! I think tyrant is a rather more apt word to describe him.

"Since he came into power, there has been nothing but hardship and injustice for the common people. His dictatorial regime has meant that people can barely express an opinion without fear of the consequences. Spies and armed men are to be found everywhere, while he continues with his sinful pastimes - wine, gambling and harems is all we ever hear of him.

"Imam Hussein and the real Muslims were deeply dismayed by this state of affairs and longed to be rid of Yazeed. The receipt, one day, of two bags of letters from the people of Kufa, in Iraq, made them determined to do something to change things. It seemed that the state of oppression was particularly bad in Kufa, for the letters contained nothing but tales of torture and tyranny. Misery and poverty were increasing and nothing was being done to alleviate the people's awful condition, since it seemed that public money was being spent on the dictator's own personal comfort. In addition to the letters there was a petition containing well over a thousand names, pleading for help from Imam Hussein.

"Imam Hussein's first reaction, may Allah be pleased with him, was to leave for Kufa immediately, for he was deeply concerned about their distress. His followers, too, were equally sympathetic and felt that something had to be done. Some of his advisers, however, were rather more sceptical; they reminded Imam Hussein of the Kufans' renowned cowardice when it came to direct confrontations. 'If negotiations don't work out', they told the Imam, 'and it becomes necessary for military action to be taken, which knowing Yazeed is very likely to happen, you will not be able to rely upon them. A few casualties and they will soon surrender to him.'

"Letters came from his cousin Abdullah ibn Ja'far, and even from the governor of Madinah imploring him not to go, but still Imam Hussein, may Allah be pleased with him, decided that he could not just let the matter drop; so it was arranged that his cousin, Muslim bin Aquil, would first visit the city. He would see whether the situation was really as desperate as was made out and also whether, in the event of battle being necessary, the Kufans would be prepared to stand up and fight.

"A message was received by Imam Hussein, may Allah be pleased with him, sometime after Muslim's departure, informing us that he had reached Kufa safety and easily. He said that he had been met happily by the people of Kufa who could hardly believe that he had come. The situation in the city was bad, it seemed, and help was much needed. Muslim bin Aquil also added that he had been given firm assurances from the people that they could be depended upon totally if it came to fighting. He advised Imam Hussein to come quickly.

"The Imam read the message gladly and began at once to make preparations to leave for Kufa. What he did not know, and indeed as we ourselves have only recently discovered, was that not long after Muslim's message was sent, Yazeed had come to know of what was occurring in Kufa - no doubt through his spies.

"Immediately this was discovered, Yazeed sent some of his men down to the city. It took very little pressure, I'm sure, to extract from those cowardly people the nature of Muslim's visit and his exact whereabouts. Muslim was at that time inside a mosque filled with people where, no doubt, discussions were taking place about the approaching conflict which was nearer than perhaps any of them realised.

"Yazeed's men, including Ubaidullah bin Ziyad - the governor of Kufa, arrived at the mosque fully armed.

Within a short space of time those unreliable, cowardly people, who had only very recently been giving assurances of their valour, deserted the mosque. Muslim and his two small sons were left all alone to face Yazeed's men and their evil weapons.

"They were murdered brutally within that mosque! It seems that in their fear of Yazeed those evil sinners seemed to have forgotten any fear (and a far greater fear it should have been) of Allah. Murder in the house of God! It is a matter of great shame.

"So here we had a situation where Imam Hussein, may Allah be pleased with him, with little more than a hundred people, including women and children, was fast approaching Kufa, utterly reliant on the false promises of the people of Kufa, while his beloved cousin already lay dead on the floor of a mosque, due to the cowardice of these very same people. And Yazeed, now prepared for their arrival, had thousands of armed men stationed in readiness: It could only spell disaster!

"In order to relate to you exactly what occurred during the days that followed, I will read to you a letter from one of the female servants who was with Imam Hussein's party. My wife received it only a few days ago - heaven only knows how the poor woman managed to send it in her present situation," said the old man. Taking out the many sheets of paper which made up the letter, he began to read:

'"Assalamu alaikum Sister,' - the letter began - 'ill troubles have befallen us since I saw you last. Tragedies and misfortunes have ensued, and even now we are in a terrible predicament; I don't even know whether this letter will reach you or not.

'But no! It will not do for me to start like this, I must return to the beginning of our journey to make sure you understand fully what has occurred.

'You will remember clearly the day of our departure. Even then we were a small group - perhaps a hundred or so, many of us just servants, or women and children. As you know, Imam Hussein, may Allah be pleased with him, brought his whole family with him, save one daughter who was too ill, and I ask you now to comfort her as best you can when she finds out what has taken place.

'Anyway, our small company set out on horseback that fateful night with enough provisions for a few days, carried by some camels. Within a few hours we had reached the desert and were heading North, ever northwards, towards Kufa. We were fortunate to meet up with a large number of bedouins who, on hearing of our destination, decided to join our group. Thus our numbers increased. At first the travelling was delightful. We were all in high spirits and hopeful for the future. At that time distance seemed no obstacle and the air was cool, fresh and clear. Under the moonlight the sand, in every direction as far as we could see, gleamed as if it were smooth water on a great silver tray. Except for the noises of the horses' and camels' harnesses and hooves there was not a sound to be heard.

'This seemed to last forever. Then there came a time when there was no moon any longer. We seemed to ride in the darkness, under a canopy of twinkling stars, for hours and hours. At last the eastern horizon began to grow light, and we stopped to do the dawn prayer, before continuing on our journey. Then suddenly the sun rose and everything changed in a moment. The grey sand turned to yellow and twinkled as if it were strewn with diamonds. On our left the shadow of our company, enormously long, kept pace beside us.

'The heat soon became very intense. I noticed it for the first time when I had to slip down and walk; as my sandals touched the sand, the heat from it struck up into my face as if from the opening of an oven door, and as time passed it grew worse and worse.

'After combining the noon and mid-afternoon prayers, on again and on…Thus it continued, until we eventually came to a place called Saffah. There we ate some food and drank a little water. It so happened that we came to meet with the well-known poet, Fahrduq. This poet knew much about the people of Kufa, and when Imam Hussein, may Allah be pleased with him, pressed him to describe their nature, he reluctantly replied that while their hearts were with us, their swords were not.

'This was saddening to us, but as the Imam said, "The matter now rests with Allah - His Will will be done."

'After a very short rest we went on again: same noises, same smells, same glare, till at last our shadows began to stretch out on our right, and then to grow longer and longer until they seemed to stretch out to the eastern end of the world. Slowly the sun drew nearer to the western horizon, and then at last the sun was down and, thank Allah, the merciless glare was gone, although the heat coming up from the sand was as bad as ever, as we discovered when we stopped to pray the sunset and night prayers together.

'Every day that passed was identical, as was every night. Our only diversions were occasional stops at small villages. It was at one such place, known as Dhurad, that we received the most terrible news: We came to learn that our messenger, our beloved Imam's cousin, Muslim bin Aquil, had been publicly executed by Ubaidullah bin Ziyad, the governor of Kufa, and nobody had done anything to stop it. A great fear sprang up inside me and tears filled my eyes.

'Our companions pleaded for our return to Madinah, for the fickleness of the Kufans had been proved. Imam Hussein, may Allah be pleased with him, considered this proposition for some time, but when the relatives of

Muslim bin Aquil protested that they would never abandon the journey until Muslim's death had been avenged, there was no other way to go but forward.

'At this point Imam Hussein, may Allah be pleased with him, addressed the bedouins who had joined us soon after the beginning of our journey. He told them that it would be best if they now left the party for, of course, they could not have known that such a thing would happen; he added that there would be no resentment on our part. Accordingly they went on their way, and so as a result our numbers fell once more and we were once again a small entourage, the majority of us family members.

'After this unfortunate setback, we continued on our journey, until at last one day we reached Iraq, and then, further on, a place called Qadsia.

"We are here!" proclaimed Imam Hussein, may Allah be pleased with him. "We have reached Qadsia - we are on the outskirts of the province of Kufa. Thank Allah for delivering us this far!"

'But it seemed he spoke too soon, for after riding a little further on, with our hearts singing, we were met by Yazeed's army…

'It seemed that the army stretched out forever. There was no way we could get past them without using force. For my own part my heart sank; I had not anticipated such a calamity. The men, however, had been aware that such a situation might arise, and did not seem too alarmed.

'After remaining where we were for a while, Imam Hussein, may Allah be pleased with him, strode bravely forward. Approaching from the other side was a strong burly man, with thick black moustache; he was obviously the leader of Yazeed's army.

"So it has come to this has it?" said Imam Hussein sadly. "Yazeed won't even let me enter Kufa for negotiations."

"Our beloved leader has no need for talking - all is well in Kufa," replied the troop leader whose name was Hur bin Yazid. His voice was deep and authoritative, but his eyes seemed to betray a look of awe now that he was in the presence of Imam Hussein. It was the same expression of awe that we felt when we looked at him - we seemed to see the Prophet Muhammad, may the blessings and peace of Allah be on him and on his family, in him - and the proximity of heaven if we were true Muslims, or the depths of hell if we were untrue.

'The two men continued discussions for a short while, with Imam Hussein urging Hur to allow us to enter Kufa, while Hur obstinately refused.

"I am under strict orders not to allow you to pass through," he said, "and I have been commanded by the governor of Kufa to take you before him."

"My appearance before that man is not possible before my death," exclaimed Imam Hussein firmly.

"But I must take you to Ubaidullah bin Ziyad," repeated Hur.

"But by Allah, I will not go with you," replied the Imam. "I bow to no one but Allah."

"Well then, it seems we must proceed to Kufa, but I must escort you, although I have no orders to fight against you. I wish to avoid any conflict, so I am going to write a letter to Ubaidullah bin Ziyad, and I suggest you do the same."

'Imam Hussein, may Allah be pleased with him, agreed to do this.

'Although we were all feeling disheartened at this state of affairs, we never gave up hope, for the Imam talked to us, inspiring us with the truth of Allah.

'At one point he said, "Falsehood is being deliberately acted upon. There was no-one in Kufa who could prevent this wrong doing. It is high time a believer should try to defend the truth for the sake of Allah. It is a wrong action in itself to accept oppressors."

'The truth of this statement so filled our hearts that one Zaheer bin al-Yaqin exclaimed, "We would rather die with you than live for ever!"

'Our spirits were much raised now and shortly afterwards a messenger, Qais bin Mashiq, was sent to our supposed allies in Kufa, whom we hoped would come to our aid soon.

'When we were told, "The Kufans will not come, message or no message," our reply was simply, "Where there is a will there is a way, and insha'Allah the Kufans will indeed come."

'Following this, we set up camp in a safe place and waited, even though deep inside we really knew that the chances of the Kufans coming to our aid was small. Still, even a small chance is still a chance.

'A day passed in the glaring heat and frequent trips were made to the nearby lake which was behind us, for water was greatly needed to keep up our strength.

'Our men were preparing for battle and although they were skilled, strong and brave, they were nevertheless only few in number. Many times the horrible thought that the Kufans would not show up crossed my mind. What would happen then? How could our hundred or so men possibly fight against this army of thousands? How easy it would be for Yazeed to pour away the blood of the Muslims like water. I banished the thought from my mind at once and went to pray, almost pleading with Allah to send the people of Kufa soon. The distance was short, so why shouldn't they come?

'Come they should have, but the next day they weren't there. Instead more of Yazeed's men were placed around us. We were taunted with warnings that the people of Kufa would never come, and that we were fools for putting our trust in such cowards.

'Imam Hussein, may Allah be pleased with him, was warned continually by Hur, telling him to turn back now before even that became impossible. He repeatedly said that if war was waged, then we would surely all be killed.

'To this Imam Hussein replied, "Do you try to scare me with death? I am proceeding ever towards it, but death does not mean humiliation for a brave person, when his intention is genuine and he fights in the way of Allah."

'Of course we were still moving slowly forwards towards Kufa, and eventually came to a place known as Azib ul Hiyanat. We met the long awaited Kufans here - but not the thousands that we expected - only four men on horseback.

'Imam Hussein, may Allah be pleased with him, received them gladly and enquired of them what was happening in Kufa. Sadly it seemed that the poet Fahrduq's words were true, for the horsemen told us that the city people had been offered a bribe to fight against us, and that they had willingly accepted the bribe, even though it was they themselves who were responsible for our presence there in the first place.

'Our hearts were further made heavy by the news that our messenger, Qais bin Mashiq, had been assassinated by Ubaidullah bin Ziyad. Tears filled our eyes at this news and we prayed ardently for a swift journey to Paradise for him.

'Now it seemed that doom was impending and there was a darkness and heaviness in the air. This feeling was further deepened when we were told of a dream that Imam Hussein had had, after leaving a place called Qasar bin Maqtal. In the dream he had seen a horse-rider moving ahead of him and crying, "People move onward and death, too, moves with them."

'This could of course be nothing other than an intimation of our approaching deaths. A dreadful fear filled us, but we could not help but remember the words that the Imam had said to his son 'Ali: "There is no doubt that we are in the right, and so we should not fear death."

'Some days later the letter which Hur had sent to Ubaidullah bin Ziyad was answered with his reply. The message was very curt, stating that our company was not to encamp in any place other than in an open desert area, and that should these orders be disobeyed, there would be sharp penalties. This ultimatum was a heartless one. The heat was terrible enough as it was, without this further added cruelty. It was then that it was suggested by Zaheer that perhaps it would be better to fight the force already present, rather than waiting and then having to combat a much larger army later on. But Imam Hussein, may Allah be pleased with him, of course did not want to initiate any war or killing, so this idea was rejected. Instead we pitched our tents not far from the river Euphrates in a small village. Ironically the village's name was Aqr, meaning fruitless. The next day we continued slowly forwards in the direction of Kufa, the army of Yazeed menacingly keeping pace with us and watching us, like a pack of wild dogs circling their prey.

'We arrived at Karbala, which is very close to Kufa, on the 2nd of Muharram. The river Euphrates was still in front of us, but relatively a long way off, with a hill to struggle over before it could be reached.

'It was then that the trouble really started, for the following day Umar bin Sa'd arrived with an army of 4,000 men.

'Both Imam Hussein, may Allah be pleased with him, and Hur, whose army had been escorting us since our arrival at Qadsia, desired an amicable settlement to this unfortunate situation, and when Imam Hussein pointed out that he had only come as a result of the Kufans' repeated requests, and that he was prepared to returned to Madinah since they obviously didn't want him here, it seemed that we might be able to turn back.

'But it was too late to turn back now. "You can not leave,"

we were told by Umar bin Sa'd. "Our beloved Khalif Yazeed has decided that until the Imam and his followers here have acknowledged him as their leader, there can be no return to Madinah for them."

'This was an absolute outrage to all of us. We just could not believe it. I can still recall the prickle of hot angry blood rushing to my skin when I heard these words.

"Surely you are not speaking the truth?" said Imam Hussein incredulously. "I know I am speaking for all my people when I tell you that this is an absolute insult to us Muslims. By Allah, I think I would rather die than have that sinner Yazeed as my Khalif!"

"I would watch your words carefully if I were you," replied the army leader menacingly. "What you say might just happen!"

'Something in his voice made me realise that he meant what he said. But at the same time Imam Hussein, may Allah be pleased with him, was deadly serious also.

'Discussions were to no avail now. Yazeed was resolute. I still find it incredible to think that a so-called Khalif would stoop so low as to threaten the life of the Prophet's grandson, especially when it is known that he once said, "Whoever loves these two" - meaning Hassan and Hussein - "and their father and mother" - meaning 'Ali and Fatima - "will be with me on the Day of Rising." But still, this was the situation.

'We were all more or less agreed that we could not yield to such a tyrant and that even if we were to fight and perhaps die, then this would be better than to continue to live as traitors to Islam and to Allah.

'Our spirits were subdued now as we faced our impending doom, but an unexpected occurrence helped to revitalise our hope once more: Imam Hussein was met by Hur and almost three hundred men who proclaimed that they had come to join our side.

"It is true," said Hur. "We cannot stand by and let this happen. At first I thought that perhaps you would turn back and that all this could be avoided, and then when you didn't, it still seemed impossible to me that Yazeed would even dare touch you. But now it appears that he is even more unscrupulous than I had imagined. Therefore my men and I have come to join forces with you, for while our fear of Yazeed is undoubtedly great, we fear and love Allah far more.

'Imam Hussein beamed at this. "This is wonderful, Hur," he said, clasping the man by his shoulders. "You and your men will surely be given Paradise for doing this. I do not have to tell you that we need all the men we can find and at least now we have more men."

"Against their four thousand or so," observed Hur.

"Have no fear," Imam Hussein replied, "Allah will give us strength."

'He said this bravely, but we could feel that he was more than a little aware of the probable outcome of taking on this enormous army.

'What I had feared most had come.

'It was decided that the battle was to commence on the 10th of Muharram. Many in the army were surprised that Imam Hussein had taken up the challenge - I suppose they imagined that he would accept Yazeed as Khalif and leave quietly, but he had not done that. He had kept his word to Allah to establish Islam, even though it meant fighting in Muharram.

"I am loath to fight during this month," he told the army. "It is the first month of the new year and fighting of any sort is forbidden during it, but since I have no other alternative, it is all I can do."

'This was said a few days before the battle, and that night Imam Hussein, called all the people in our camp together:

"I realise that you all feel obligated to me," Imam Hussein began. "Some of you may no doubt feel that you do not wish to be involved in such a one-sided battle. I do not blame you if you feel this way, for our situation has changed a great deal since we departed from Madinah - misfortunes have befallen us that we could never have anticipated. To you all I say this: if you feel you do not want to fight in this battle then I now give you this opportunity to leave for escape is still possible.

"I shall allow you to leave in such a way that it causes no embarrassment. I will dim the lanterns and then those who wish to depart may do so."

'Having said this Imam Hussein proceeded to darken the camp. A few scuffling sounds could be heard, and after about ten minutes the lanterns were lit again. For some reason I had expected nearly everyone to leave, but no, most people still remained. Two, maybe three, had left us to our fate.

"Good," smiled our beloved leader, "You have chosen the true path."

'The battle, as I have already told you, was to take place on the 10th. On the 9th a terrible thing happened, in which Umar bin Sa'd and his men exceeded themselves in cruelty and inhumanity. I have spoken before of the burning heat which was constant at that time, and I have also told you of the lake which was now a few miles behind us and which had supplied us with our daily water requirements, and of the river Euphrates which still lay ahead of us, over a long hill.

'What Umar bin Sa'd chose to do was to station his men in such a way that access to both the lake and the Euphrates was completely blocked off from us.

'We could not obtain any water!

'Horror struck us - there was a battle to be fought only the next day - and we had no water! It was impossible. Already the hot sun was blazing down upon us; the sand was baking hot, so that it was hard even to walk upon it with thick sandals. Water was required all the time, for thirst was ever-present - I could feel my own throat dry and my lips parched already, and I wasn't even going to be fighting.

'And what would happen when injuries took place on the battlefield? There would be no water to soothe the wounds - infection would set in. It was an absolute nightmare to even think about it. Wasn't it enough that they had blocked the way both to Kufa and Madinah from us? Wasn't it enough that the Kufans hadn't aided us? Wasn't it terrible enough that war was being waged with the Prophet's grandson? And now this - no water!

'Neither protests nor anger could make any difference now. The battle was to take place, with no water on our side.

'The 10th of Muharram came at last, after a torturous, thirsty night. Prayers had been going on all night, with pleas to Allah for strength to face this most awful of battles.

'Before the fighting began, Imam Hussein, may Allah be pleased with him, gave a short speech to all around him. His lips were dry and cracked and he spoke with difficulty, having to gulp several times to retain at least some moisture. Perspiration poured from his face, but his eyes remained bright and calm and his words rang true.

'He reminded Umar bin Sa'd's men of the wrong that they were doing - not only to us, but to themselves also.

"Look at me," he told them. "Do you know who I am? I am descended from our beloved Prophet Muhammad, may Allah bless him and grant him peace. I am his grandson! Do you forget so easily the words he spoke about his family, words of which you must all be aware?" Imam Hussein proceeded to quote much of what the Prophet had said, reminding them of the error of their ways - that anyone who fought against or harmed the Prophet's descendents would surely invoke the wrath of Allah; that any hopes that any of them might have of going to the Garden would most certainly be replaced with the vision of eternal Hell.

'Time and time again the Imam asked, "Is it fair for you to kill me in total disregard of the respect due to me? Is it right for you to receive me with unsheathed swords?"

'He reminded the Kufans present that they themselves had called him there. He quoted their letters. When there was still no reply to this he asked, "You wrote these letters; do you not recall?"

'And then, subhan'Allah, one of the Kufans called out that they had never written any such letter.

Incredulously Imam Hussein, may Allah be pleased with him, shouted out, "What a blatant lie!"

'Indeed, we were all shocked that they could speak like this, so easily denying their part in the matter. I wondered at how the army that opposed us could just stand by and listen to this speech and still not let us go. But it seemed that their hearts had turned to stone, that their eyes were blind, and their ears deaf.

'In our camp, Imam Hussein's sister, Zainab - now having learnt that war could not be avoided - was lamenting and weeping for she could not bear the thought of losing her brother in this way. We tried to calm her down but it was to no avail. Of course only the Imam could pacify her. He told her to have forbearance and perseverance and to reconcile herself to Allah's will.

'And now there was no way out of this battle. It had become apparent that all efforts to avoid it had been in vain. War was inevitable.

'Umar bin Sa'd strung his bow and shot forth an arrow towards our camp, shouting out, "Be witness, I have shot the first arrow!"

'And so the battle at Karbala commenced.

'As is our custom in warfare, we began with single combat. Two slaves from the other camp approached. From our camp Abdullah bin Amir al-Kalbi rose to meet their challenge. A strong, tall man, he truly looked a warrior.

'Masha'Allah, he fought like a warrior also; it only took a few blows to put his rivals to death. His wife, Umm Wahhab, was so exhilarated by this that she almost rushed out onto the battlefield herself. She was of course stopped by the Imam, who while commending her valour reminded her of the fact that only men should fight. We, in the camp, nonetheless congratulated her bravery.

'Although our army was very small - only seventy-two men in total (thirty-two horsemen and forty foot soldiers) - their wits were sharp. A trench was dug behind our camp and filled with fire so that attack by the enemy from the rear was not possible. In addition, our frontline men held their spears out straight and, lining them up against the enemies' horses legs, caused the horses to be so frightened that their riders could not advance.

'After this, single combat continued for a short while, but since every challenger who came forward from Umar bin Sa'd's army was killed by our men, soon the enemy proceeded to commence the main battle.

'Obviously, being a woman, I was not in the thick of the battle at all, but safely tucked away, not seeing much at all. But I could still hear, although it was difficult to discern much amid the thunder of horses' hooves and the clash of swords, together with the occasional battle cries. We had messengers though, telling us of all that was going on.

'It turned out that wherever our thirty-two horsemen struck they caused a lot of damage to the enemy. Unfortunately this did not last long because their enemies sent for reinforcements, and very soon five hundred arches were shooting at our horses, crippling them and thus rendering them useless.

'Later on we discovered, much to our dismay, that our brave warrior, Abdullah bin Amir al-Kalbi, had been killed. His valiant wife took the body of her dear husband into her arms and while wiping the dust from his face, she too was killed.

'Disappointments were coming thick and fast now, and to add to this, we received a further blow in that the enemy decided that they would give us no time for prayers. This angered and dismayed us greatly, but it seemed the battle had to carry on.

'At last the night approached and the fighting ceased. Imam Hussein, may Allah be pleased with him, and our men returned. They were nearly all badly wounded and everywhere there was blood, blood, blood. There was no water, however, to wipe away the blood and dust and soothe the torture. Some of the men were finding it hard to breathe and were exhausted, not only from fighting, but also from the intolerable heat. Water was all they craved, but there was none.

'It turned out that the brave Hur and the majority of his men had been killed during that day, so that of our company, very few fighting men remained. There are very few words that could really describe the exhaustion and depression that pervaded the camp that night. This was further increased by the fact that numerous dead bodies had to be buried. There was a silence over us that seemed to spell out impending doom. Except for our prayers, not much else was spoken, for of course we had then - and always will have - Allah to turn to in times of need. He is enough for us, the best Protector and the best Guardian. And those who die fighting in the way of Allah are not dead. They are with Allah, in Paradise.

'The second day of the battle came. Our few remaining warriors strode bravely out, trying to disguise their frailty and weakness after having been denied water for so long.

'Sadly, the battle was over very very soon. One by one all of our men were killed, until finally only Imam Hussein, may Allah be pleased with him, remained. No one dared touch him. They merely crowded around him. In our camp only the women and children remained. Imam Hussein's young son 'Ali, could bear it no longer and rushed out onto the battlefield. Although he fought valiantly, he was no match for an army of thousands and was soon killed. Soon another young lad stepped out onto the battlefield. He was a strikingly beautiful youth and attacked with immense force, but within minutes he too had been killed, with the cry of "O Uncle!" on his lips.

'It seemed terrible that such young blood was being shed, but at least they had had a few years of life. What happened next, however, was beyond excuse: a small boy had been born in the midst of all the fighting, to one of the women in our camp and naturally Imam Hussein wished to call the Adhan in his ears as is customary. But just as he was doing this, an arrow sped from the enemy and pierced the small infant's throat. The baby died immediately and deep shock stunned us, as the poor mother lamented over the body of her newly-born, newly-killed son.

'Now it seemed that there was no way out for the Imam; very soon it seemed that he too would be killed. But still no one dared to lift a finger to hurt him. "Why don't you kill him?" yelled 'Umar bin Sa'd, their commander; but nobody would approach him.

'Imam Hussein was already in deep pain, although he had not been wounded or injured, because he had been without water for so long. He longed for water, as we all did, and in a vain attempt to fetch some, he struggled over towards the river and tried to get past the guards.

The heartless tyrants, however, would not let him anywhere near the thirst-quenching water that he sought. And then the first blow hit him - some evil man shot forth an arrow which just nicked Imam Hussein's neck. Luckily he pulled it out immediately - he was not dead. But he was angry! He called out, "Who dared to do this to me? Do they not realise that Allah will not be angry at anyone's death more than mine?"

"Don't listen to him!" shouted 'Umar bin Sa'd. "Kill him!"

'Once more Imam Hussein, may Allah be pleased with him, was surrounded and it was as if he was in a cage. But instead of it being a cage where the humans were outside and an animal inside, it was as though the animals were all on the outside looking in at the proud God-fearing man who stood on the inside, dignified, never forgetting Allah, and never regretting his fight against injustice.

'Oh sister, sadly his death was inevitable. A disgusting, evil man sprang forward and in a single blow decapitated him. Horror and grief filled our hearts when we were told this - we had not believed such cruelty possible. It seemed that the murderer was not only evil, but also mad too, for he leaped around laughing and congratulating himself - when in fact he had just ensured his place in the Hellfire for ever!

'After this, all chaos broke out - clothes and possessions

were looted and plundered, and even after his death, the Imam was not left alone, for his body was stripped of its clothes.

'Such sickness of mind, such inhuman heartlessness, I've never before encountered in my life, and I hope never to meet with it again. Thankfully, we women were left alone in our tents and not taunted or tortured.

'The next thing we heard of was just as awful; we could hear the sound of the thundering of horses' hooves outside and we later discovered that Imam Hussein's precious body was being trampled over again and again and mangled to pulp.

'Nausea overwhelmed me and I was physically sick - the thought of what they did to him almost breaks my heart even now.

'It must have been far worse still for the Imam's sister, Zainab - she seemed utterly broken, and there was not an eye that did not shed tears at the sight of her heartfelt laments.

'After this evil, it seemed no cruelty was impossible for our enemy. The heads of all our people who had been killed during the battle were now severed; they were seventy-two in number and were taken before Ubaidullah bin Ziyad, who thought it was all very amusing.

'I will not attempt to describe our grief, because it is

impossible to put it into words, and all I wish to do is block it out.

'All I can say is that we have been carried off by Yazeed's men and have endured many hardships. Hopefully one day we will return to Madinah, insha'Allah.

"Surely we come from Allah, and surely to Him we return.""

"The letter ends here my son," said the old man sadly, "with our leader's life."

The traveller's heart was heavy after listening to this terrible story. After several minutes' silence he looked up at his elder - in whose eyes tears glistened - and said, "You were right when you said these were dark days. Never have I heard of such shameful conduct. How could one Muslim be so cruel to the next?"

The old man could find no words to answer this and only shook his head slowly. There are real Muslims, and then there are those who only pretend to be Muslims.

"There is a lesson to be learnt from this you know," said the young traveller earnestly. "We need to be better Muslims - we have to take Allah's word and learn it and understand it and act on it. Only then can we begin to find real peace and happiness; not only in this life but in the next life also."

"You are absolutely right my son," said the old man, "and do you know what? I think what you are saying is beginning to happen. People are trying harder to be true Muslims - not just here in Madinah, but everywhere."

The young man nodded in agreement "As I have travelled I have seen it. Please Allah let these improvements last. For as they say - after darkness comes light."

With this thought in mind the two men, one young, one old, went to the mosque to pray.

May you, dear reader, also take heed of these words, for in these troubled times for Muslims everywhere, we must not lose hope, but strive ever forward to live in accordance with Allah's guidance, and to fight against falsehood.

Zayd ibn Arqam related that the Messenger of Allah, may Allah bless him and grant him peace, said, "I implore you by Allah! The people of my House!" three times. We asked Zayd who constituted the people of his House, and he said, "The family of Ja'far (a son of Abu Talib), the family of 'Uqayl (another son of Abu Talib), and the family of al-'Abbas." (Muslim).

The Prophet, may Allah bless him and grant him peace, said, "I am leaving you something, taking hold of which will prevent you from going astray: the Book of Allah and my family, the People of my House. So take care how you follow me regarding them." (At-Tirmidhi).

The Prophet, may Allah bless him and grant him peace, said, "Recognition of the family of Muhammad is freedom from the Fire. Love of the family of Muhammad is crossing over the Sirat. Friendship for the family of Muhammad is safety from the Fire."

One of the 'ulama said, "'Recognition' in this case means recognising their place in relation to the Prophet, may Allah bless him and grant him peace. Recognition of that brings with it recognition of the rights and respect that are due to them because of it."

'Umar ibn Abi Salama said that, "Allah wants to remove impurity from you, people of the House", (33:33) was revealed in Umm Salama's house. The Prophet, summoned Fatima, Hasan and Hussein and enfolded them in a garment and 'Ali was behind him. Then he said, "O Allah! These are the people of my House, so remove all impurity from them and purify them completely!" (At-Tirmidhi).

(Ash-Shifa of Qadi Iyad: II, 3.5, p241.)

And may the blessings and peace of Allah be on the Prophet Muhammad, his wives, and on his family, and on his companions, and on all who follow him. Amin.